S0-ARX-890

HOUGHTON MIFFLIN HARCOURT

JOURNEYS

My Journey Home
Family Connection

Grade 5

HOUGHTON MIFFLIN HARCOURT

Credits
Illustrations: © Houghton Mifflin Harcourt Publishing Company

Photo Credits: page 24 Corbis, 40 Jupiter, 46, 56 Photo Disc/Getty Images.
All other photos owned by Houghton Mifflin Harcourt.

Copyright © by Houghton Mifflin Harcourt Publishing Company

All rights reserved. No part of this work may be reproduced or transmitted in any form or by any means, electronic or mechanical, including photocopying or recording, or by any information storage or retrieval system, without the prior written permission of the copyright owner unless such copying is expressly permitted by federal copyright law.

Permission is hereby granted to individuals using the corresponding student's textbook or kit as the major vehicle for regular classroom instruction to photocopy entire pages from this publication in classroom quantities for instructional use and not for resale. Requests for information on other matters regarding duplication of this work should be addressed to Houghton Mifflin Harcourt Publishing Company, Attn: Contracts, Copyrights, and Licensing, 9400 South Park Center Loop, Orlando, Florida 32819.

Printed in the U.S.A.

ISBN: 978-0-547-92897-5

If you have received these materials as examination copies free of charge, Houghton Mifflin Harcourt Publishing Company retains title to the materials and they may not be resold. Resale of examination copies is strictly prohibited.

Possession of this publication in print format does not entitle users to convert this publication, or any portion of it, into electronic format.

5 6 7 8 9 10   0982   18 17 16 15 14 13
4500402225

My Journey Home
Family Connection

To the Teacher

My Journey Home: Family Connection has been developed to involve parents and other family members in their children's reading progress. Designed to accompany *Houghton Mifflin Harcourt Journeys*, this booklet provides new, motivating activities for children and family members to share.

For each of the 30 lessons in *Journeys*, a weekly menu gives suggestions for interactive games, activities, and reading passages. The activities support classroom reading vocabulary and skills in ways that enable parents to work along with their child. Additional suggestions for more challenging activities, Internet use, and appropriate books for independent reading are also provided. The quick, on-the-go activities fit easily into busy home schedules and make learning a fun and important part of family life.

Use the letter on the next page at the beginning of the school year to introduce families to *My Journey Home: Family Connection*. Personalize the letter by signing your name. Then, as the year progresses, encourage families to share in the benefits of home involvement.

My Journey Home
Family Connection

Dear Family,

Please join me in helping your child become a more confident, successful reader by sharing the activities from **My Journey Home: Family Connection** each week with your child. These pages provide quick, fun ideas for building on the vocabulary and reading skills we're learning in class.

The weekly **Family Connection** pages make reading a regular part of family life. They include on-the-go, high interest games, activities, and reading to share. Daily suggestions are given, but these activities can be used anytime during the week.

Please note the optional suggestions for challenge activities, book titles, and Internet activities. Also look for Tips that make it easy to support your child's learning.

Also, here are other ways to make reading a family affair:
- ◆ Read and discuss books together, even after your child can read on her or his own.
- ◆ Visit the library together as often as possible.
- ◆ Let your child see **you** reading!

Begin with a few **Family Connection** activities each week. Then watch your child become a more motivated reader!

Sincerely,

My Journey Home
Family Connection

This week your child is reading "A Package for Mrs. Jewls," a humorous story about what happens one day at a very unusual school.

Vocabulary on the Go   In the story, a character has to carry a heavy box up thirty flights of stairs. With your child, recall an experience when you or your child had a hard time carrying or transporting something from one place to another. See how many of these words you can use.

staggered   **wobbled**   **shifted**   **struggled**   **collapsed**

What's the Story?   Have your child play the role of Louis the yard teacher to tell about his day. Ask questions like the ones below to find out more about the unbelievable school where he works.

- What is Wayside School like?
- Who is Mrs. Jewls? What is she like?
- What problem did you have to solve?
- What happened when you delivered the package to Mrs. Jewls?

Home, Tall Home   Together, imagine what homes would be like if every room was on a separate floor. Then talk about where each room would be located and what life in a house like that would be like.

Help your child draw a picture of a house with a different room on every floor. Ask your child to label each room.

What's Up with Gravity? Mrs. Jewls explains gravity to her class in an unusual way. Read and try this experiment with your child.

An Experiment with Gravity

What You'll Need
- a small rubber ball
- a clean, empty mayonnaise jar
- a tabletop, floor, or other flat, smooth surface

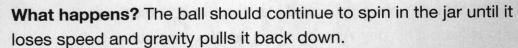

1. Put the ball on the tabletop and place the jar over the ball. The mouth of the jar should be flat on the table.
2. Spin the jar in a small, fast, circular motion, keeping its mouth flat on the table. It may take a few tries to get the ball spinning in the jar, but keep trying.

3. When the ball is spinning in the jar, lift the jar above the table.

What happens? The ball should continue to spin in the jar until it loses speed and gravity pulls it back down.

DAY 5

Famous Scientists Did Sir Isaac Newton really "discover" gravity from an apple? Did Galileo really drop cannonballs from the Leaning Tower of Pisa? Together, find more information about these scientists.

CHALLENGE Help your child make a poster that tells about something they learned about Newton or Galileo.

Book Links
- *Smart Dog,* by Vivian Vande Velde
- *Millicent Min, Girl Genius* by Lisa Yee   CHALLENGE

Internet Challenge "A Package for Mrs. Jewls" is a story from the Wayside School series by Louis Sachar. Check out Sachar's books online together, including *Dogs Don't Tell Jokes* and *Holes.*

My Journey Home
Family Connection

This week your child is reading *A Royal Mystery,* a play about a young girl who discovers she is a princess while at summer camp.

Vocabulary on the Go   This week's selection takes place at a summer camp. Using the vocabulary words listed below, have your child describe what it might be like to live in a tent for a week of summer camp.

disturbing   squashing   numb   collapsed   shifted   wobbling

Getting Along   The two characters who share a tent and become teammates in *A Royal Mystery* seem to come from different backgrounds and appear to be at odds with each other. Talk to your child about a time when he or she did not get along with someone at first, and ask if they were able to work out their differences. Ask your child to think about what people who come from different backgrounds can do to try to understand one another.

   Role-play with your child to practice working out differences in a peaceful way.

Trophy Time   In this week's selection, the campers at Camp Katahdin compete in events in the hope of winning the annual trophy. Ask your child to share a time when he or she won an honor, or share a goal he or she has of being recognized for an accomplishment or ability. Tell your child about a time when you were recognized for or achieved a goal.

Expression Matters With your child, focus on the morning routine in your home and see how to use two different formats to tell about it.

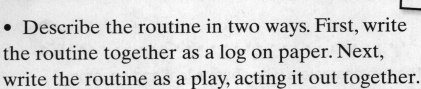

- Review that *A Royal Mystery* is a play and that a play differs from other forms of literature in that characters express their thoughts and feelings directly to the audience.

- Talk about the morning routine in your house with your child. What do the members of your family do when they first wake up? How do they interact when they prepare to begin their day? What are their moods like?

- Describe the routine in two ways. First, write the routine together as a log on paper. Next, write the routine as a play, acting it out together.

- How do the two formats differ? Talk with your child about which method provides an opportunity for greater expression.

City and Camping In this week's selection, Rena is not used to camping and living in nature. She is similar to someone who would live in the city. Althea is used to camp and does not mind sleeping in a tent, cleaning up after the horses, and showering in the shower room. Have your child explain where he or she would enjoy spending the summer— in the city or at a summer camp.

Book Links
- *The Princess and the Pea,* by Hans Christian Andersen
- *The Princess Diaries,* by Meg Cabot **CHALLENGE**

Internet Challenge Go to the library or search the Internet to find out more about the origins of playwriting.

My Journey Home
Family Connection

This week your child is reading *Off and Running*, a realistic story about a class election between two candidates with very different ideas and personalities.

Vocabulary on the Go   The two student candidates in the story have to give a speech in front of their classmates. Together, recall a time when you or your child had to perform or speak before an audience. Try to use some of the following words.

hesitated   gradually   scanned   stalled   prodded

Alike But Different   Family members are alike in many ways, but they can be very different, too. With your child, discuss ways that two members of your family (or two family friends) are similar and different.

Help your child make a chart to compare how the two people you discussed are alike and different.

Little Ideas, Big Impact   What are some ways to make your child's school a better place? Could more student art be displayed? Would a class or school read-along event help build community? Together, brainstorm a list of ideas.

Vote for Me Read and discuss the following selection with your child.

Campaign Slogans

When candidates run for President of the United States, they often come up with short, catchy statements to help convince people to vote for them. These slogans often get put on bumper stickers, posters, or campaign buttons. The slogans remind voters of what the candidates stand for.

In 1864, President Abraham Lincoln used this slogan for his campaign: "Don't swap horses in the middle of the stream." At that time, the United States was in the middle of the Civil War. President Lincoln was trying to convince voters that it would not be a good decision to switch Presidents in the middle of a war.

In 1928, Herbert Hoover used this campaign slogan in his campaign: "A chicken in every pot and a car in every garage." President Hoover was trying to convince voters that if he was elected President, everyone in the country would prosper.

More recently, President Barack Obama used the slogan "Yes We Can!" for his presidential campaign. What kind of feelings do you think President Obama wanted to inspire? What do you think he was trying to say about himself?

Vote for Me Ask your child to imagine that he or she is running for president of the fifth-grade class. Then help your child design a bumper sticker with a slogan for his or her campaign.

Book Links
- *No Talking,* by Andrew Clements
- *All of the Above: A Novel,* by Shelley Pearsall **CHALLENGE**

Internet Challenge Help your child search the Internet for tips and ideas about giving an effective speech or presentation to an audience.

My Journey Home
Family Connection

This week your child is reading *Double Dutch: A Celebration of Jump Rope, Rhyme, and Sisterhood.* This nonfiction selection tells about a middle school's jump rope team.

Vocabulary on the Go Watch a team sports event together. Talk with your child about the event, and the skills and teamwork the players show. Use some of the following words in your conversation.

competition   mastered   element   unison   intimidated

And Then What? In *Double Dutch,* a team travels to a new place to participate in a competition. With your child, talk about a time when you made a trip for a special purpose or to visit a new place. Take turns recalling the events of the trip in the order in which they happened.

Help your child make a comic strip about the events of the trip. In captions or speech bubbles, use words and phrases that tell about the order of events, such as *first, next, after that,* and *finally.*

Get Moving What's a physical activity that you and your child can enjoy doing together? Make up a new dance, take a neighborhood walk, play catch, go on a nature hike, or blow up a balloon and bat it back and forth!

A New Game   Read and discuss this selection with your child.

Basketball's Beginnings

On college campuses, in school gyms, and on courts around the country, you can find a basketball game in progress. Fans flock to watch favorite teams play this fast-paced sport.

James Naismith surely couldn't have imagined that the game he invented for a physical education class in the winter of 1891 would become one of the most popular games in the history of sports. As a teacher at the YMCA International Training School in Springfield, Massachusetts, Naismith was asked to come up with indoor games to keep his students active during the cold winter months. When Naismith introduced this new basket game to his class, one student was said to remark, "Huh. Another new game."

Naismith's game, in which players tossed a ball into a peach basket nailed to a balcony ten feet above the floor, quickly grew into today's exhilarating game. In Springfield, the Naismith Basketball Hall of Fame honors this great game and the greatest players who have played it.

DAY 5

Playground Games   Talk together about games kids play at recess or on the playground. Do they play kickball, four square, wall ball, or freeze tag? Share stories about the games you enjoyed playing in school, too.

Book Links
- *In the Year of the Boar and Jackie Robinson,* by Bette Bao Lord
- *Jim Thorpe: Original All-American,* by Joseph Bruchac **CHALLENGE**

Internet Challenge   Help your child search the Internet for websites and video clips of jump rope and double Dutch teams and competitions. Talk about the kinds of skills these athletes possess.

My Journey Home
Family Connection

This week your child is reading a realistic story called *Elisa's Diary*. It tells about the struggles a young girl faces when she leaves her home in Puerto Rico to live in a new country.

Vocabulary on the Go   Ask your child to think about what it would be like to be new to the United States and not know much English. Talk about how people in a new country might feel if they don't speak the language of that country. Try to use some of these words.

embarrassed   **typically**   **supposedly**   **obvious**

A Lesson Learned   In the story, Elisa learns that working with someone else can help you solve a problem or overcome a fear. With your child, talk about books, movies, or TV programs where a character learns a similar lesson.

Here in the U.S.   One character in the story tells about the quetzal bird. This bird symbolizes power and appears on the national flag of Guatemala as an emblem of national liberty. What ideas are important to people who are citizens of the United States? Discuss with your child what makes our country special.

Work with your child to make a flag with symbols that represent some of the ideas you discussed. What symbols will you use? Why did you choose them?

Join Forces   Read and act out this scene together. In it, Marcus has written a poem about a snowstorm. His sister Kelly enters.

The Contest

KELLY: Can I read your poem, or would you be embarrassed? *(Marcus hands her the poem. She reads it and smiles.)* Hey, I like this. You sure have a way with words. Is it homework?

MARCUS: *(sheepishly)* No, it's for a contest. The winner gets a free class at the arts center. I just think it needs something more, like an illustration.

KELLY: Well, I took a bunch of photos during that huge blizzard last year. You could use one of those.

MARCUS: But only one person can enter. We can't split a class.

KELLY: You're the poet, so you would enter. The photo would just be a gorgeous extra. Besides, I've already taken a class at the center—how do you think I became such a great photographer? Come on, let's go on a photo hunt!

Famous Teammates   Together, brainstorm a list of famous partners, such as the Wright Brothers, or Lennon and McCartney. Help your child find books or websites to learn about one or more of these teams.

Book Links
- *Seeing Lessons,* by Spring Hermann
- *Fame and Glory in Freedom, Georgia,* by Barbara O'Connor **CHALLENGE**

Internet Challenge   Together, search for a website about Puerto Rico. Discuss how Puerto Rico is similar to and different from where you live. What would you like and not like about living in Puerto Rico?

My Journey Home
Family Connection

This week your child is reading an informational text about the work of biologists to study the tree kangaroo.

Animal Facts Talk with your child about your favorite animals and then choose one to research. Using the Internet or animal books, find as many facts about your animal as possible. Try to find little-known information such as the following: average body temperature, number of teeth, sleeping habits.

Zoo Trip In this week's selection, *Quest for the Tree Kangaroo*, the lead biologist was inspired to study this endangered animal after visiting a zoo. Take a trip to a local zoo with your child and see what endangered animals live there, protected in environments similar to their natural ones.

  If a trip to a zoo is not possible, look through magazines or books to see what endangered animals you can find.

Vocabulary on the Go This week's selection focuses on the research and protection of endangered animals. Talk with your child about why it is important to protect animals that may be in danger of extinction. Try to use some of the following vocabulary words:

procedure   presence   outfitted   transferred   enthusiastic

Teamwork   This activity provides an opportunity for you and your child to work together to make a difference in your home or community.

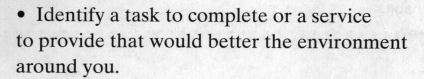

- Have your child tell how the biologists worked together to capture, study, and release the tree kangaroos.

- Talk with your child about the importance of teamwork. Share with your child a time when you worked as part of a team. Then ask your child to tell about his or her experience working with other people at school or on a team to accomplish something.

- Identify a task to complete or a service to provide that would better the environment around you.

- Work as a team with your child to complete the task you chose. Ask your child to consider what to do if members of a group do not agree with something. Discuss with your child the importance of compromise.

Save Me!   With your child, make a poster to spread the word about the need to save an endangered animal. Talk with your child to create a slogan and include colorful pictures or drawings of the animal if possible. Search the Internet for websites about endangered animals.

Book Links
- *Eyewitness: Endangered Animals,* by Ben Hoare
- *My Life with the Chimpanzees,* by Jane Goodall **CHALLENGE**

Internet Challenge Go to the library or search the Internet to find out more about the work biologists do.

My Journey Home
Family Connection

This week your child is reading *Old Yeller,* a classic story about the life of a pioneer family and the yellow stray dog who comes to mean so much to them.

Vocabulary on the Go   If you see a dog running through a park, is it *racing* or *bounding*? Look together through newspapers, magazines, and books to find pictures of dogs in action. Take turns using different words to describe how each dog is moving. Try to use some of the following words.

stride   frantic   lunging   romp

My Perfect Sibling   The main character in *Old Yeller* is annoyed by his younger brother at times. With your child, imagine that you could order a perfect brother or sister from a catalog. What qualities would you want to see in your "perfect" sibling?

Pioneer Facts   With your child, use the Internet to find information about pioneer life. What did pioneers eat? What kinds of houses did pioneers live in? What kinds of schools did pioneer children go to?

Work together to create and illustrate a "fact sheet" about the life of pioneers.

Snack Time   Read this recipe together. Then try it out to make a treat that pioneer families might have enjoyed.

No-Bake Dried Fruit Granola Bars

Ingredients

1/2 cup chopped dried fruit
(raisins, figs, cranberries, apples)
3 cups granola
3/4 cup honey   1/4 cup corn oil
1/2 cup packed brown sugar

1. Put granola and dried fruit in a large bowl. Mix together.
2. Put honey, brown sugar, and oil in a small pot. Mix together.
3. Pour the mixture into the bowl with the granola and fruit. Stir until granola and fruit are coated well.
4. Press mixture into an 8- or 9-inch square pan. Refrigerate.
5. Cut into squares. Enjoy!

DAY 5

Poodles, Dalmatians, Pugs   With your child, brainstorm a list of dog breeds. Look through library books and use the Internet if you need help. Write each breed on a card or slip of paper. Take turns choosing a card and describing that type of dog until the listener guesses the breed.

Book Links
- *Wings,* by William Loizeaux
- *My Side of the Mountain,* by Jean Craighead George   **CHALLENGE**

Internet Challenge   With your child, search the Internet for family movies about dogs. Then schedule a family movie night together.

My Journey Home
Family Connection

Your child is reading *Everglades Forever: Restoring America's Great Wetland*, a selection about a fifth-grade class's field trip to a very complex ecosystem in southern Florida.

Vocabulary on the Go Will resources like fresh water and land to grow food last forever? Or do we need to be careful about how we use them? Have a discussion with your child about reasons to protect planet Earth. Use some of these words as you talk together.

conserving guardians responsibility regulate restore

Issues and Ideas With your child, locate editorials or letters to the editor in print or online newspapers that focus on a topic related to the environment. As you read together, identify the author's viewpoint and the details he or she uses to persuade the reading audience.

Every Drop Counts In *Everglades Forever,* the students learn that most of the water people in southern Florida use comes from the Everglades. The students also learn that conserving water is important. With your child, think of ways you can conserve water in your home.

Help your child make a poster of water conservation tips and post them in your home. Help your child lead a discussion about the ideas.

A Message   Together, read the directions and complete the puzzle.

1. Read the names of habitats, types of vegetation, and wildlife listed below. Write each word in the appropriate category on the chart.

2. Use the boldface letter in each word to complete the message about the wetlands below the chart.

mangro**v**e   anhing**a**   alliga**t**or   gumbo **l**imbo tree
sl**o**ugh   man**a**tee   saw**g**rass   cormo**r**ant
swamp   ospr**e**y   prair**i**e   cabbag**e** palm

Plant Life	Wildlife	Type of Habitat

P __ __ __ E C __ THE __ __ E __ __ __ __ D __ __

Trip Favorites Have a conversation about field trips you and your child have enjoyed, and tell what was special about them. Then list three or more field trips you both think would be great to take.

Book Links
- *Graveyards of the Dinosaurs,* by Shelley Tanaka
- *Antarctica: Journey to the South Pole,* by Walter Dean Myers   CHALLENGE

Internet Challenge   Help your child identify a wetlands plant or animal that he or she would like to learn more about. Together, search the Internet for information about the plant or animal's life cycle.

My Journey Home
Family Connection

This week your child is reading *Storm Warriors*, a historical story about the efforts of African American surfmen to rescue passengers from a shipwreck during a storm off the coast of North Carolina in 1896.

Vocabulary on the Go   Have a discussion with your child about what happens in his or her school during a fire drill. As you talk together, try to use as many of the following words as you can.

critical   secured   annoyance   commotion

Personality Traits   What kinds of qualities are important for people who deal with emergencies, such as firefighters, doctors, and nurses? With your child, draw conclusions about personality traits that people in these types of professions generally possess. Help your child list details that support his or her ideas.

Weather Watch   With your child, check local newspapers, news programs, and weather websites to find the weather forecast for the week ahead in your area. Discuss the different kinds of weather that the forecasts predict.

Using your research, help your child create a weather forecast chart for the week ahead. At the end of each day, take notes on how accurate the predictions were.

First-Aid Kits   Read and discuss this article with your child.

Be Prepared for Emergencies

Emergencies can happen anytime, anyplace. Having a first-aid kit is a great way to deal with situations you don't anticipate. You can purchase ready-made first-aid kits, or you can put together your own. Here are supplies for a basic kit:

adhesive and cloth bandages
   (assorted sizes)
adhesive cloth tape
roller bandages
antiseptic wipes
antiseptic ointment or cream
latex gloves
pain relievers (aspirin,
   acetaminophen, ibuprofen)
instant cold compress

hydrocortisone ointment or cream
sterile gauze pads (assorted sizes)
oral thermometer
tweezers
scissors
flashlight and batteries
blanket
medical and emergency
   phone numbers

Many families keep a first-aid kit in their home and in the car. Check the contents of your kit on a regular basis. Discard and replace outdated contents. You never know when an emergency might arise, but if you can reach for a first-aid kit, you'll be better prepared for one!

Into the Past If you could travel back in time, what time and place would you visit? Together, discuss what you would like to see and do in the past. Use the library or Internet to find out more about your choices.

Book Links
- *Anna's Blizzard,* by Alison Hart
- *Hurricane: A Novel,* by Terry Trueman **CHALLENGE**

Internet Challenge What's the difference between a hurricane, a tornado, a monsoon, and a tsunami? Together, use the Internet to find out how these extreme weather events are alike and different.

My Journey Home
Family Connection

This week your child is reading *Cougars,* a selection about the big, mysterious cats that live in many parts of North America.

Vocabulary on the Go   What might cats think as they eye birds? Take a neighborhood walk with your child and together imagine things cats might say about birds you see. Use as many of the following words as you can.

unobserved   detecting   ferocious   particular   keen

What's the Big Idea?   Read a paragraph from a nonfiction book your child is familiar with. Tell your child what that paragraph is mostly about in one sentence. Then ask your child to name details in the paragraph that tell about the main idea.

The main idea of a paragraph is what it is mostly about.
The details tell more about the main idea.

Animals Like Us   Cougars are incredibly powerful and athletic animals that are known for their secretive habits. Are you a lot like a cougar? If not, what kind of animal are you like? Together, name some animals that are most like you and your child. Then discuss each animal's characteristics.

Have your child draw a picture of an animal that is like him or her. Then help your child to write a caption that tells how he or she is like the animal.

Fabulous Fable Together, read this fable about cougars.

The Cougar Reunion

None of the cougars could remember whose idea it was to organize it, and perhaps it didn't matter. But somehow it happened that the cougars decided to hold a reunion.

Cougars traveled from far and wide to spend time with each other. Long-separated siblings looked forward to getting reacquainted. The ferocious ones had tall tales ready to go. Even the most secretive old cats had a hankering to see buddies from their youth.

Old friends hugged and wept with joy. Mothers gushed over adorable kittens. A few males dragged dinner along as a feast for all.

But by the next afternoon, contentment flagged; tempers frayed. There wasn't enough space. Or food. "Those noisy kids are scaring off all the good eats," grumbled one cougar. "Oh, get lost," muttered a third.

There was no real discussion, but by the end of the day, all of the cougars had headed back to their own territories.

Moral: A cougar reunion probably isn't a very good idea.

Big Cats What makes a lion special? How is a tiger unique? Together, list different types of big cats, and discuss each one's characteristics. Choose one cat and look for books or websites to learn more about it.

Book Links
- *The Truth About Dangerous Sea Creatures,* by Mary M. Cerullo
- *Face to Face with Wolves,* by Jim Brandenburg **CHALLENGE**

Internet Challenge Cougars live in a range of habitats. Together, search the Internet for photos and images of cougars in their natural settings. Talk about how each habitat helps the cougar survive.

My Journey Home
Family Connection

This week your child is reading *Dangerous Crossing,* a historical story about the exciting sea voyage a young John Quincy Adams embarks upon with his father.

Vocabulary on the Go   Talk with your child about a dangerous storm you both have experienced. Why was it dangerous? What did you think was going to happen? Try to use some of these words as you discuss what happened during the storm.

distracted   viewpoint   surveyed   bracing   shattered

Causes of the Revolution   *Dangerous Crossing* takes place during the American Revolution. What events caused the American colonies to enter into war with England? With your child, make a list of events that led to the Revolutionary War. You can use the Internet or library books for help.

Passing the Time of Day   During the long sea voyage, the young John Adams took up learning French as a useful way to pass the time. What are some other useful things you might want to learn while on a long trip? Would you learn to knit, take up drawing or writing, or become a master at chess? Together, identify at least three things you would like to learn.

   How would you teach someone one of these ways to pass the time? Work together to write a simple set of directions for one of your ideas.

Fathers and Sons   Read and discuss this selection together.

Benjamin and William Franklin

John Adams and his son John Quincy had a warm relationship. But another brave colonist named Benjamin Franklin did not have such a relationship with his son William. William Franklin was present when his father famously flew a kite during a lightning storm in 1752. The two men shared many interests, but their differing political viewpoints led to a deep rift between father and son.

In 1763, William was made Royal Governor of New Jersey by King George III. William's loyalty to the king and his father's role in the American Revolution made their relationship hard. In 1776, William was arrested and jailed for supporting the British. He later made England his permanent home.

The long-standing conflict between Benjamin and William Franklin is evident in the elder Franklin's will. In it, Ben declared that his son would inherit "no more of an estate he endeavored to deprive me of." In the end, their differing opinions on politics shattered the relationship between this famous father and son.

Benjamin Franklin

DAY 5

Name the Presidents   John and John Quincy Adams both became President of the United States. How many of our Presidents can you name? Find a President whose name begins with each of the letters in this word: AMERICA. (Clue: One letter does not have a President).

Book Links
- *Sleds on Boston Common,* by Louise Borden
- *George vs. George,* by Rosalyn Schanzer   **CHALLENGE**

Internet Challenge   Help your child search the Internet for information about John Quincy Adams' life and presidency. Then work together to make a timeline about his life.

My Journey Home
Family Connection

This week your child is reading *Why Can't You Make Them Behave, King George?* a selection that gives the King of England's point of view about the American Revolution.

Vocabulary on the Go   Why did the Patriots want their freedom from England? Try to use some of these words as you and your child give reasons for the Patriots' rebellion.

repeal   **prohibit**   **objected**   **rebellious**

What's the News?   Together, read a news article or listen to a newscast about a history-making event. Then take turns naming facts about the event and giving your opinions about it.

 A fact can be proved true. An opinion is a belief or feeling.

Interview a King   Have your child take the part of King George, and act as a newscaster who must "interview" him or her. Find out the king's opinions about the troubles in the American colonies. Ask questions such as these:

- Why are the colonists angry about the tea tax?
- Why did the Boston Tea Party make you angry?
- Why are you sending more troops to the colonies?

 Help your child write some of the questions and answers in the form of a magazine article.

Tea Anyone? Read and discuss this eyewitness account from George Hewes with your child. Hewes was one of the Patriots who participated in the Boston Tea Party.

An Eyewitness Account

We then were ordered . . . to open the hatches and take out all the chests of tea and throw them overboard, and we immediately proceeded to execute his orders, first cutting and splitting the chests with our tomahawks, so as thoroughly to expose them to the effects of the water.

In about three hours from the time we went on board, we had thus broken and thrown overboard every tea chest to be found in the ship. . . .

The next morning, . . . quantities of [tea] were floating upon the surface of the water; and to prevent the possibility of any of its being saved for use, . . . small boats were manned by sailors and citizens, who rowed them . . . wherever the tea was visible, and by beating it with oars and paddles so thoroughly drenched it as to render its entire destruction inevitable.

DAY 5

Connect to the Past With your child, find books or a website giving details about the Boston Tea Party. What interesting facts can you discover? What happened to those who took part in the Tea Party?

 Book Links
- *A Young Patriot,* by Jim Murphy
- *The Fighting Ground,* by Avi **CHALLENGE**

 Internet Challenge Help your child use the Internet to find out more facts about life in the American colonies in the 1700s.

My Journey Home
Family Connection

This week your child is reading *They Called Her Molly Pitcher*, a selection about the remarkable bravery of Mary Hays, a Revolutionary War heroine known as Molly Pitcher.

Vocabulary on the Go   Do you think that soldiers in the Continental Army felt that they could win the war? Use some of these words as you exchange your opinions. Make sure you support your opinions with good reasons.

strategy   retreat   foes   revolution

Think It Over   A woman on the battlefield was an unusual sight during the Revolutionary War. Discuss some of the reasons why people at that time didn't think women should be soldiers. Do you agree with them? Why or why not?

Brave Women   Together, identify and discuss female family members, friends, or women in your community who have acted bravely in some aspect of their lives.

Help your child draw or create a "badge of honor" for one of these women. List the woman's accomplishments beneath a picture of her.

Their Stamp on History   Read and discuss this selection with your child.

Stamps Issued to Celebrate Our Country's Birthday

WASHINGTON, DC — Some heroes of the American Revolution have had their stories recorded for posterity, like Molly Pitcher. But the contributions of thousands of other valiant colonists remain unknown. To honor the bravery of four unfamiliar heroes of the American Revolution, the U.S. Postal Service issued special commemorative stamps to celebrate our country's birthday.

Brave heroes, pop culture icons, historical milestones, ethnic celebrations—all these and more have also been featured on com-memorative stamps. Since 1893, when the first such stamp was created, the Postal Service has issued new stamps to recognize subjects of national importance. Though stamps have varied greatly in shape and size and the images on them, they all serve to remind us of the unique character and history of our nation.

It's in the Mail Together, look at the stamps you've received in the mail recently. What images and information are shown? Find out about the history of postage stamps by finding information in books or on a website such as the U.S. Postal Service or the National Postal Museum.

CHALLENGE Ideas for U.S. postage stamps are accepted from the public. Help your child draw a stamp design to commemorate a person, group, or event.

 Book Links
- *This Time, Tempe Wick?* by Patricia Lee Gauch
- *The Real Benedict Arnold,* by Jim Murphy **CHALLENGE**

 Internet Challenge Together, search the Internet for information about another Revolutionary hero. Learn a few facts about how this person helped the colonies win the war against the British.

My Journey Home
Family Connection

This week your child is reading *James Forten,* a biographical selection about a young African American sailor's role during the Revolutionary War and how he became a successful businessman and an influential abolitionist.

Vocabulary on the Go   With your child, imagine that it is the late 1700s. Role-play the parts of a young person who wants to become a sailor and a ship's captain. Try to use the following words as you engage in a job interview together.

persuade   apprentice   contributions   aspects   dexterity

A Step in the Right Direction   After the war, James Forten became an apprentice to Robert Bridges and learned to make sails. With your child, think of occupations that require special schooling or training, such as carpentry, surgery, or computer programming. Together, identify some of the steps a student would need to follow to learn this job. Use words such as *first, next, after that,* and *finally* in your discussion.

What Do You Want to Be?   Ask your child to name a job that he or she would like to do some day. What kinds of things would your child have to learn to do?

   Help your child write a want ad for the job that you discussed. Make sure the qualifications for the job are listed.

What's in a Song?
Read this description about the song "Yankee Doodle" with your child. Then sing the song together.

Once taught to children as a lively nursery rhyme, British soldiers brought "Yankee Doodle" to the colonies, using its rhythm to keep step as they marched. Later, when relationships between the British and American colonists became strained, the British soldiers made up new, insulting verses for the tune. Instead of taking offense, though, the colonists changed "Yankee Doodle" into a song reflecting pride in the Patriot cause.

Yankee Doodle

Verse:

Yankee Doodle went to town,
A-riding on a pony,
He stuck a feather in his cap,
And called it macaroni.
(Chorus)

Chorus:

Yankee Doodle, keep it up,
Yankee Doodle dandy,
Mind the music and the step
And with the girls be handy.

Sing Along Help your child make up verses for "Yankee Doodle." Create verses that describe Revolutionary War figures, such as James Forten in this verse, or modern day heroes.

Oh, Jimmy Forten went to sea / To fight the Patriots' battles,
'Twas caught by British in a fight / But saved by playing marbles!

Book Links
- *Everybody's Revolution,* by Thomas Fleming
- *Give Me Liberty,* by L. M. Elliott **CHALLENGE**

Internet Challenge
With your child, search the Internet for information about African American inventors, such as Benjamin Banneker, George Washington Carver, Lonnie Johnson, and yes, James Forten.

My Journey Home
Family Connection

This week your child is reading *We Were There, Too!*, a nonfiction selection that tells about two young heroes of the American Revolution.

Vocabulary on the Go   Ask your child to imagine what it was like to be a soldier in the American Revolution. Talk about a typical day in his or her life. Use some of these words as you talk.

personally   efficient   lacked   tedious   organize

Then and Now   Talk about what life might have been like during the American Revolution. Compare things such as how people dressed, what their homes were like, and how they traveled from place to place with these same things today. Use the Internet or library books for help.

Help your child make two drawings that compare life at the time of the American Revolution and life now. Ask your child to write captions for each drawing.

Interview a Hero   Have your child take the part of Joseph Plumb Martin or Sybil Ludington. Then ask your child questions about his or her experiences during the American Revolution. Ask questions such as:

- What did you do during the war? How did you feel about what you did?
- How did you feel about what the British did?
- How did you feel after the colonists won the war? Why?

A Midnight Visitor   Read and discuss this diary entry with your child. It tells about the night that Paul Revere rode from Boston to warn the Patriots that the British soldiers were coming.

April 19, 1775   I was sound asleep last night when I heard a yell outside our house. It must have been well past midnight.

Mother and Father were asleep, too. But they jumped out of bed when they heard a man ride up on his horse. I ran to the window. I could see Father talking to the man. The man's words sent chills up my spine—The British are coming!

The man rode away towards one of our neighbor's farms. Father ran back into the house. He pulled on his boots and grabbed his rifle. He was ready to go in less than a minute. I stood there as Father hugged Mother. Then he came and hugged me and my brother, too.

After Father left, Mother explained to us what was happening. Father was a Patriot. He was going to fight the British. I went back to bed and tried to sleep. I was proud of Father, but I couldn't stop worrying about what might happen to him.

Write It Down Talk about an exciting experience that your child has had. Then help your child write a diary entry to tell about what happened and how he or she felt about the experience.

Book Links
- *Midnight Rider,* by Joan Hiatt Harlow
- *Johnny Tremaine,* by Esther Forbes   **CHALLENGE**

Internet Challenge Help your child search for a website to find information about another hero of the American Revolution.

My Journey Home
Family Connection

This week your child is reading *Lunch Money*, a realistic story about a young boy who creates and produces his own comic book series.

Vocabulary on the Go Are books and stories with illustrations more fun to read? Or are stories better when you have to use your imagination to picture characters and events? Discuss these questions with your child. Use some of these words as you share your opinions.

mental   feature   incredibly   villains   suspense

Why a Comic? Together, name some comics that you and your child are familiar with. Then discuss why an author would write these comics. Does the author want to give you information? entertain you? persuade you to agree with him or her?

Your Inner Superhero Every superhero has some kind of extraordinary power that serves a special purpose. With your child, create superheroes based on yourselves. What unusual power would each of you possess? Why?

Work together to draw pictures of yourselves in your superhero gear. How can your picture best show your special powers? Help your child add labels or captions to the drawings.

Interview with a Villain Read, discuss, and perform this interview with a comic book villain together.

Talking to Baron von Brouhaha

INTERVIEWER: Baron, we all know that you can appear and disappear at any time. How did you develop this power?

BARON: *(slyly)* Let's just say that my mental and physical abilities are far superior to those of the average human. My powers allow me to set off chaos, or a brouhaha, at will.

INTERVIEWER: How does it feel to be one of the most feared beings on the planet?

BARON: *(sighs)* Well, honestly, it's a lonely job. I think the hardest part is being so misunderstood.

INTERVIEWER: Misunderstood? Could you elaborate?

BARON: Raising a ruckus is just plain fun. I don't see how people can't get that. *(impatiently)* Don't we all need a break sometimes? I see myself as providing a service to mankind!

INTERVIEWER: *(incredulous)* You see causing distress and disturbance as a good thing? You must be mad!

BARON: I'm getting a little mad right now! I think you need a little, ahem, *brouhaha*, right now! *(wickedly)* HA HA!!!

INTERVIEWER: Aaah! I can't move! Someone! Anyone! Help!!

So Bad He's Good What makes a good bad guy or gal? Together, think up ideas for a super villain. Name and draw him or her.

Book Links
- *Stan Lee: Creator of Spider-Man,* by Raymond H. Hiller
- *Beowulf,* adapted by Gareth Hinds **CHALLENGE**

Internet Challenge Andrew Clements has written many novels. Together, use the Internet to find out more about books by Clements, such as *Frindle, No Talking,* and *A Week in the Woods.*

My Journey Home
Family Connection

This week your child is reading *LAFFF*, a science fiction story that tells what happens when a girl who enters a writing contest learns that a classmate has invented a time machine.

Vocabulary on the Go   One of the characters in the story is a young inventor. What are some recent inventions that you enjoy using? With your child, identify new products and inventions that make your life easier. Try to use the following words in your discussion.

impressed   produced   original   concentrate

Tell Me About It   Ask your child to think of a favorite science fiction movie or TV show. Where does it take place? Who are the characters in it? What problems do the characters have? How do the characters solve their problem?

Dream Up an Invention   Are you always late getting out of the house? Do you wish you had a robot to sort and organize household clutter? With your child, brainstorm an idea for a fanciful invention that could solve a specific everyday problem.

Help your child create a diagram of the invention. Then create an acronym for it. An acronym is a word formed from the initial letters of a name. For example, *LAFFF* stands for *Lu's Artifact for Fast Forward*.

A Taste of Asia The characters in *LAFFF* share tasty Asian dishes, such as spring rolls and humbow, a kind of barbecued pork roll. Read the following recipe with your child. Then use the ingredients to make a traditional Asian dipping sauce.

Asian Peanut Sauce

Ingredients
1/2 cup peanut butter, chunky or smooth
2 tablespoons teriyaki sauce
2 tablespoons sesame oil
2 garlic cloves, pressed or minced
1 tablespoon grated fresh ginger
dash of hot sauce (optional)
salt and pepper to taste

1. Put all the ingredients together in a bowl.
2. Stir them together until well mixed.
3. Serve as a dipping sauce for fresh vegetables, such as baby carrots, sliced cucumber, green or red peppers, and celery sticks.

What Was It Like? The plot of *LAFFF* involves a school writing contest. How can entering a contest be both exciting and nerve-wracking at the same time? Together, recall contests or competitions you have each been in. Share your thoughts about what the experiences were like.

Book Links
- *Magic in the Margins*, by W. Nikola-Lisa
- *The Fire Thief*, by Terry Deary **CHALLENGE**

Internet Challenge Help your child search the Internet to learn about real inventions that changed people's lives in the last hundred years. What tasks did the inventions make easier? How did people do the tasks before the inventions?

My Journey Home
Family Connection

Your child is reading *The Dog Newspaper*, an autobiographical selection that tells about the author's first efforts at writing and publishing a newspaper when she was young.

Vocabulary on the Go   How do you find out about the news? Do you prefer to read newspapers or magazines, watch television news programs, or use online sources? As you talk with your child about different types of news sources, use some of the following words.

publication   **household**   **edition**   **background**   **insights**

Fact or Opinion?   Newspaper stories include both facts and opinions. With your child, browse a front-page story in a recent newspaper. Together, locate several facts and opinions in the article. Then read an editorial together and find several facts and opinions in it.

 A fact is a statement that can be proven. An opinion is a statement that tells a thought, feeling, or belief that cannot be proven.

For Animal Fans   While *The Dog Newspaper* only lasted for a few issues, many magazines today focus on specific types of pets and other animals. Together, browse the magazine racks at a local library or bookstore, and see how many different magazines about animals you can find.

 Help your child create a catchy name for a magazine about animals and design a cover that would appeal to potential readers.

Animals in the News The author's first newspaper article tells about a puppy who is saved by soldiers after its mother is killed during a war. Together, read and discuss this newspaper article about another orphaned animal.

Unlikely Friends

KENYA, AFRICA – Amidst the destruction caused by the Indian Ocean tsunami on December 26 comes a heartwarming story of survival and unusual friendship.

When the aftereffects of the tsunami washed a family of hippos out to sea, a baby hippo was left behind on a reef, orphaned and terrified. Corralled by a group of human onlookers, the hippo was transported to the Haller Park sanctuary in Mombasa. Upon its release there, the baby hippo immediately sought refuge with a 130-year-old male giant tortoise living in the sanctuary.

Within a short time, the unlikely duo seemed to form a close bond. The baby hippo, named Owen for the rugby player responsible for saving him, now stays close to Mzee, the ancient tortoise, at all times. According to the manager of the sanctuary, the two animals are now inseparable companions. These improbable animal friends are visited daily by a continuous stream of park visitors, eager to witness a positive outcome from the natural disaster that rocked the region.

A Family Story In her autobiography, the author of *The Dog Newspaper* tells that she learned that stories need to be fresh and interesting. With your child, choose an exciting event that you would include in a biography about your family. Why would readers like to hear about in this tale? How can you make it more interesting to read?

Book Links
• *Dear Mr. Henshaw*, by Beverly Cleary
• *Media Madness*, by Dominic Ali **CHALLENGE**

Internet Challenge Help your child search the Internet to find a recent story about animals in the news. If possible, browse different articles that tell about the story. Discuss the ways that the stories are similar and different.

My Journey Home
Family Connection

Your child is reading *Darnell Rock Reporting*, a realistic story that tells how one student's newspaper article results in a local controversy.

Vocabulary on the Go With your child, role-play a situation in which a driver returns to his or her car to find a parking officer writing a ticket for expired time on the parking meter. Try to use the following words in your dialogue.

violations   exception   minimum   urge

Is It Persuasive? In order to persuade readers, a writer needs to supply reasons that support his or her ideas. Together, locate and read an editorial on a topic that interests your child in a print or online edition of a newspaper. Identify the reasons the author offers to back up his or her position. Are the author's reasons convincing? Why or why not?

CHALLENGE What is your child's opinion about the topic? Discuss the reasons he or she feels this way.

Helping Out What are different things people can do to help people in a community? Together, make a list of different ways of helping. You can also search some local community websites to see if there are programs that are helping people in your area.

De-stress Out! Before giving a speech, as Darnell Rock does, it helps to relax. Together, read, discuss, and try these relaxation tips.

Slow Down, Feel Better

Want to feel less stressed? Try these tips to help you feel less tense and more confident.

Tip 1: Calm Your Mind

- Get comfortable and sit quietly. Close your eyes.
- Create a mental image of a restful place or scene. Focus on this image until you feel calmer.

Tip 2: Relax Your Body

- Tense and relax each muscle group, in this order: feet, calves, thighs, abdomen, back, arms, hands, neck.
- Hold your mouth open wide, then relax your mouth.
- Squeeze your eyes shut, then open them.

Tip 3: Breathe Deeply

- Inhale slowly, taking a full, deep breath. Hold for five seconds.
- Exhale slowly through your mouth. Repeat ten times.

DAY 5

Listen Up Together, look into upcoming talks and programs in your area that are of interest to your child. Use local newspapers, online resources, or postings at schools and libraries. Attend one together, and then discuss how effective each of you thinks the speaker was.

Book Links
- *The Daring Nellie Bly,* by Bonnie Christensen
- *Second Fiddle: Or How to Tell a Blackbird from a Sausage* by Siobhán Parkinson **CHALLENGE**

Internet Challenge Darnell suggests selling food from a community garden. Together, search the Internet to find gardens and farmers' markets near you. Plan a visit to see what is grown or sold there.

My Journey Home
Family Connection

This week your child is reading *The Black Stallion,* an adventure story about the special relationship that forms between a boy and a black stallion as they fight to survive after a terrifying shipwreck.

Vocabulary on the Go   The setting of *The Black Stallion* is a remote island. Alec and the horse survive on seaweed and the little fish Alec can catch. Create an adventure story with your child built around the theme of survival. Try to use the following vocabulary words:

piercing   *quivered*   *savage*   *heave*   *delicacy*

Career Goal   Walter Farley, the author of this week's selection, began writing *The Black Stallion* when he was only 16 years old. He combined his passion for horses and writing to create a successful series of books. Talk with your child about ways he or she could tap into an interest or talent.

If the discussion sparks excitement, research what steps are necessary to make your child's goal a reality. Conduct a search on the Internet of careers associated with your child's interest.

Animal Workers   Animals that help take care of people are called *service animals*. These animals do much more than provide the comfort of regular pets. Service animals are specially trained to perform tasks for people with certain disabilities. Some animals guide people who cannot see, alert people who are deaf, help pull wheelchairs, and even protect their owners if they have medical emergencies, such as seizures. Ask your child if he or she has ever seen a service animal before. Where? What service did the animal provide?

Try, Try Again   This activity will help your child understand the importance of perseverance and of not getting discouraged when things in life are difficult.

Alec, the boy stranded with the black stallion, wants to ride the horse. The horse is not receptive to this idea at first and throws Alec off its back. Alec tries again, only to be whirled into the air. Eventually, the black stallion trusts Alec and allows him to ride on his back. What do Alec's repeated attempts to ride the horse show about his personality? Talk with your child about the importance of not giving up in frustration when things become difficult. Share with your child a time when you became frustrated with something and the steps you took to overcome that frustration. Have your child make a plan of behavior to follow the next time he or she has difficulty doing something.

DAY 5

Creature Comforts   In many hospitals, dogs come with their owners to visit patients in their rooms. In fact, some dogs hop right up on the beds to snuggle! Why do you suppose hospitals allow this? Talk with your child about the comfort that pets can provide to humans and the effect these feelings may have on healing.

Book Links
- *Dog Training for Kids,* by Carol Lea Benjamin
- *The Cay,* by Theodore Taylor **CHALLENGE**

Internet Challenge   Go to the library or search the Internet to find out more about how to train a dog or another animal to obey commands.

My Journey Home
Family Connection

This week your child is reading *Tucket's Travels,* historical fiction about an older boy who must save two children from an outlaw band by fleeing into the desert.

Vocabulary on the Go What would you do if you were on a daylong wilderness hike, and a huge rainstorm suddenly blew in? Talk about what you can do to seek shelter. Try to use as many of these words as you can.

> **salvation**   **stunted**   **evident**   **pace**   **seep**

A Change in Plans Like Tucket's adventure, sometimes life can take unexpected turns. With your child, recall a trip that ended up differently from your original plan. Use photos or scrapbooks if you need help jogging your memory. Together, review the events of the trip in the order in which they happened.

CHALLENGE Help your child create a comic strip to retell the trip events in sequence.

A Desert Hike Together, play a game by naming things you would need if you were hiking across a desert, like Tucket and the children. Take turns saying *I'm going to hike across a desert, so I will need ____.* Have your child keep a list of the items named. Later, review the items and discuss whether early settlers or pioneers would have had these items at the time in which they lived.

Measure the Rain Together, investigate rainfall in your area by making a rain gauge. (An adult should cut the plastic bottle.)

Homemade Rain Gauge

What You'll Need

- a clean, clear 2-liter plastic bottle
- a knife or shears that can cut plastic
- duct or masking tape
- a waterproof marker
- ruler
- water

1. Cut off top third of the bottle with a knife or shears.
2. Push the top of the bottle into the bottom to make a funnel. Tape the edge where the two parts meet.
3. Fill the bottle with just enough water to form a flat bottom for the rain gauge. Mark this water baseline as "0 inches."
4. From this "0" baseline, use a ruler to mark inches directly up the side of the bottle. Number each inch and half-inch mark.
5. Secure the gauge to something sturdy, in a place open to rain but out of direct sun.
6. Keep a log of how much rain collects over weeks or months.

Personality Profile What traits does teenager Francis Tucket need to care for two children on their long journey? Together, create a "personality profile" of what an ideal teenage caretaker would be like.

Book Links
- *The Abernathy Boys,* by J. L. Hunt
- *He Will Go Fearless,* by Laurie Lawlor **CHALLENGE**

Internet Challenge Together, search the Internet for information about cloud formations, including cumulonimbus clouds from the selection. What kinds of clouds do you see where you live?

My Journey Home
Family Connection

This week your child is reading *The Birchbark House*, a historical story that tells about an encounter a young Native American girl has with a bear family.

Vocabulary on the Go   With your child, imagine that you have come across a bear cub while on a walk in the woods. Suddenly, the cub's mother appears. Try to use these words as you describe the scene together.

> deserted   reasoned   upright   bared

Now imagine that the mother bear begins to speak! Draw an illustration and write what the bear might say, using the words *astonished, nerve,* and *banish.*

CHALLENGE

Brothers and Sisters   The actions of the main character in the story are influenced by her unhappiness with her older sister. With your child, think of some folktales or stories in which a character's actions are affected by a sibling. What message is the storyteller trying to give in each one? Compare and contrast the different lessons the characters learn in each example.

Sniffing Out Scents   When the young girl in the story is pinned by a bear, she thinks of all the scents the bear might smell on her, and how the bear smells to her. Play a game with your child. Take turns closing your eyes and smelling different items from your refrigerator. Can you guess what the items are?

A Legend   Read and discuss this Native American tale together.

Bear and Chipmunk

One day, Bear was lumbering through the forest, looking for food. As he lifted fallen tree limbs and heavy stones, he marveled to himself, "I am the strongest creature in the land. There is nothing I cannot do!"

A tiny voice chattered, "Oh, is that so? You are not so strong that you can stop the sun from rising!"

Bear looked down and saw a little chipmunk laughing at him. "I can do that! The sun is not stronger than me! I will show you tomorrow!"

Chipmunk laughed at Bear again, and ran to tell all the animals about Bear's foolishness.

Bear stayed awake all night. The next morning, the sun rose as always. Chipmunk squealed with delight! In a flash, Bear angrily pinned Chipmunk with his huge paw. Chipmunk escaped, but Bear's claws left three scars on Chipmunk's back.

From that day, chipmunks wear these signs to remind them why animals should not make fun of one another.

An Honored Creature   Bears are revered by many Native American tribes. With your child, think about why this might be. Consider what bears are like, what they do, and how they behave. You can use the Internet or library books for help.

Book Links
- *The Birchbark House,* by Louise Erdrich
- *The Buffalo and the Indians,* by Dorothy Hinshaw Patent   **CHALLENGE**

Internet Challenge   In the story, Omakayas enjoys a sweet maple candy. Help your child search the Internet for information about how maple syrup and maple syrup candy are made.

My Journey Home
Family Connection

This week your child is reading *Vaqueros: America's First Cowboys,* an informational selection that tells about the history and traditions of the first cowboys of Spanish Mexico.

Vocabulary on the Go Take a walk or drive around the area where you live. Discuss its history or the history of the nearest town. Who first lived there? How did the people who lived there survive? Try to use some of these words in your conversation.

extending   residents   flourished   acquainted   sprawling

Holiday Special In Mexico, *El día del charro* celebrates the history and culture of rodeos and riders with parades, religious services, exhibitions, and music. Discuss holidays in the United States with your child. What are some details that make each holiday special?

Help your child use reference books or the Internet to research another Mexican holiday. Work together to make a poster that tells about its history and how the holiday is celebrated.

Working with Animals The vaqueros rode horses and cared for cattle and steer. What are other professions that deal with animals? Play a game in which you and your child each make a list of three or four of these occupations. Then take turns describing or acting out an occupation for each other to guess.

Spanish to English Together, answer the clues with one of these words: *avocado, bronco, burrito, hammock, lasso, machete, poncho, tuna.* (These Spanish words are now common in English.)

CLUE 1: You can wear this cape-like covering to keep you warm in the cold or dry in the rain. What is it?

CLUE 2: Rodeo riders challenge themselves to ride this kind of bucking horses. What is it?

CLUE 3: You might find rice, meat, cheese, and vegetables inside one of these. What is it?

CLUE 4: This is a swinging couch or bed that is usually made out of rope. What is it?

CLUE 5: This is a huge cutting tool that explorers often use to cut a path through thick jungle trees. What is it?

CLUE 6: This rope with a loop in the end is used on ranches to catch runaway animals. What is it?

CLUE 7: This large ocean fish is a popular food. Lots of kids eat sandwiches filled with its meat. What is it?

CLUE 8: Many people think this fruit is a vegetable. It looks like a dark pear but has a rich, buttery meat inside. What is it?

DAY 5

Look It Up Many English words have Spanish origins. Together, use a dictionary to find the Spanish origins of these common English words: *alligator, cafeteria, cargo, hurricane, patio, savvy, stampede, tornado.*

Book Links
- *The Journal of Joshua Loper, A Black Cowboy,* by Walter Dean Myers
- *Who Was First?* by Russell Freedman **CHALLENGE**

Internet Challenge Together, search the Internet for information about explorers mentioned in the selection, such as Columbus, Hernán Cortés, or Francisco Vázquez de Coronado, as well as others.

My Journey Home
Family Connection

This week your child is reading *Rachel's Journal: The Story of a Pioneer Girl,* a historical story that tells about the challenges of daily life on the Oregon Trail.

Vocabulary on the Go   Together, discuss what it might have been like to travel by covered wagon on the Oregon Trail over 150 years ago. Try to use each of the following words as you discuss things you might see or experience on your trip.

mishap   rustling   quaking   surged   torment

A Big Move   In the story, a young girl and her family are on the move to a new life in California. What are some reasons that families decide to move to an entirely new place? What are some effects of a big move? With your child, plot out some reasons families might move. Then think of and record what might happen as a result.

> Together, choose a place in a different part of the country where you might want to move. Help your child write a list of pros and cons about moving to the new place.

Two Different Takes   In a journal, a writer records his or her thoughts and perspectives on events and occurrences. But do two people recall an event in the same way? With your child, write separate journal entries that tell about an everyday event you share together, such as a meal or an outing. Then compare your entries. Are you surprised?

A Valuable Guide   Read and discuss this selection together.

The Prairie Traveler

Students of history are often amazed that travelers on the Oregon Trail ever reached their destinations. Believe it or not, many pioneers prepared for trips much like tourists today; they relied on traveler's guides and referred to them along the way.

One of the most useful and popular guides was *The Prairie Traveler: A Handbook for Overland Expeditions*, written by Randolph Barnes Marcy, a captain in the U.S. Army. Published in 1859, the *The Prairie Traveler* was packed with information that could save pioneers time, energy, and even their lives. How to fix a broken wagon wheel? Ways to ford a river? What to do in a storm? *The Prairie Traveler* covered all these topics, and more.

Marcy's long career working for the military on the frontier provided him with practical knowledge about every aspect of preparation and survival. No doubt, countless pioneers were grateful that Marcy shared his knowledge; more than a few lives were likely saved by a handy copy of *The Prairie Traveler*.

Essentiality Imagine a long journey you might take together. **Silently and separately**, think about and list five essential items—things you would *have to take*. Then share and discuss your lists of must-haves. What items are on both lists? Which things are surprising?

Book Links
• *A Covered Wagon Girl,* by Sallie Hester
• *Into a New Country,* by Liza Ketchum   **CHALLENGE**

Internet Challenge In her journal, Rachel describes a buffalo stampede. Help your child search the Internet for information about this amazing animal that once ruled the prairie.

My Journey Home
Family Connection

This week your child is reading *Lewis and Clark,* a nonfiction selection that tells about the famous Corps of Discovery expedition and its travels westward to the Pacific coast.

Vocabulary on the Go   Lewis and Clark traveled across the continent of North America. Look at a map of your city or town with your child. If you were going to walk across your town, which route might you take? How difficult might the trip be? As you talk, use some of these words.

expedition   **barrier**   **despite**   **trek**

What's the Point?   The author of this week's selection tries to make the reader feel what it was like to be with Lewis and Clark. Together, look for articles in magazines or newspapers that tell about someone's life or accomplishments. Discuss the author's purpose for writing the article. How does the author feel about the subject? Look for words and phrases the author uses that tell his or her viewpoint.

   An author's purpose may be to inform, to entertain, to explain, or to persuade. An author may have more than one purpose, too.

Plants or Animals?   Lewis and Clark created a vast catalogue of the native flora and fauna they found. Take a walk together and take an inventory of the plants and animals around your neighborhood. You may want to photograph or sketch what you see.

   Work together to create a chart or display about the flora or fauna you found. You can use the photos or sketches you made. Use books or the Internet to find out more information to include on your display.

Sweet Treat

Sweet Treat Lewis and Clark found many berries but probably never had this treat. Together, read the directions, and then try it out.

Berry Freeze Pops

Ingredients

1 cup each of 3 types of berries such as blueberries, strawberries, raspberries, or huckleberries

1/4 cup lemon juice

1/3 cup sugar   10 popsicle sticks

10 small plastic cups   aluminum foil

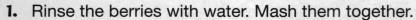

1. Rinse the berries with water. Mash them together.
2. Add lemon juice and sugar to the mashed berries and mix or puree in a blender. (Only adults should operate the blender.)
3. Pour an equal amount of the mixture in each of the cups.
4. Cover each cup with a square of foil, folding the edges. Poke a popsicle stick through the foil. The sticks should stand upright.
5. Put the pops in the freezer overnight or until they are solid.
6. Remove the foil, peel off the cups, and enjoy!

On the Team Talk together about why Sacagawea was so important to the Lewis and Clark expedition. In what ways was Sacagawea's heritage valuable? What skills and experience did she share? How was her journey different from the journey of Lewis and Clark?

Book Links

- *Railroad Fever,* by Monica Halpern
- *Sweetgrass Basket,* by Marlene Carvell **CHALLENGE**

Internet Challenge Together, search the Internet to learn more about Lewis and Clark's route. Which present-day states did they cross? What rivers and other geographical features did they encounter?

My Journey Home
Family Connection

Your child is reading *Skywoman's Rescue*, a myth that tells about the creation of the Earth and new life, including its first people.

Vocabulary on the Go   If you were a nature photographer, which animals would you photograph? Where would you look for the animals? What would they be doing? Try to use some of these words as you discuss the animals and the habitat where you find them.

scanned   gorgeous   sweeping   gradually   identical

Look It Over   This week your child is also reading a selection about animals that includes a lot of visual information, including photographs and captions. With your child, look for magazine articles about animals. Then work together to list the different visual features, such as photos, captions, maps, and diagrams. Summarize what each feature tells you about the subject.

Storytellers   The myth your child read is in the form of a play. Most myths like this one were originally in story form. These stories were handed down from generation to generation by storytellers. What are some stories that you and your child know that have been handed down? What do the stories tell about?

   Together, choose a story you both know. Take turns telling the story. How were the retellings the same? How were they different?

More on Migration Read and discuss this selection with your child. It tells about a bird that spends much of its life moving.

Frequent Fliers

Many birds are migratory, traveling from place to place to breed and overwinter. The Arctic tern, however, beats out all the competition. Rarely seen by humans except during nesting seasons, Arctic terns travel more than 22,000 miles each year!

These medium-sized birds enjoy two summers each year, as they travel from the Arctic regions of North America, Europe, and Asia to the seacoasts of the Antarctic. They live for about 30 years; in a lifetime, therefore, the average Arctic tern may travel more than 500,000 miles—a distance comparable to flying to the moon and back!

Arctic terns

Arctic terns primarily eat fish and other marine creatures they catch on the wing—or even steal from other birds. Their aggressive behavior extends to their parenting style, too. These tough birds fiercely defend their nests by mobbing and attacking any and all intruders. If you ever are lucky enough to see a colony of Arctic terns, keep your distance, or you may soon find yourself in flight (or fight)!

An Incredible Bird Together, use the Internet or other sources to find photos of Arctic terns. List adjectives to describe them, and work together to use the adjectives in sentences to tell about Arctic terns.

Book Links
- *Gray Wolf, Red Wolf,* by Dorothy Hinshaw Patent
- *Weather Legends,* by Carole G. Vogel **CHALLENGE**

Internet Challenge Help your child search the Internet for information about other animals that make long or unusual migrations, such as whales or caribou. Learn a few amazing facts about their trips.

My Journey Home
Family Connection

This week your child is reading *Mysteries at Cliff Palace,* a play about a boy who hopes to solve a mystery while taking a guided tour with his family at Mesa Verde National Park.

Vocabulary on the Go   With your child, role-play the parts of a museum director and a detective as they discuss the mystery of an item missing from a museum. Use as many of the following words as you can in your scene.

stunned   realization   checking   resemble   critical

What a Character   Have your child name a favorite TV show or movie. What are some traits of the main characters? Are they curious? silly? hard-working? lazy? How do these characters handle the problems they face in the show? Together, talk about the lesson the producers want the audience to understand, and whether or not the lesson relates to real-life experiences.

Uncovering the Past   How do archaeologists learn about past civilizations? With your child, use library books and websites to investigate what archaeologists do and how they form theories about the lives and activities of people who lived long ago.

Together, search the Internet for information about archaeologists and a current archaeological dig. Then help your child create a want ad to find qualified workers for the project.

Protect the Park Read and discuss the following newspaper article with your child.

Thistles Threaten Park

MESA VERDE NATIONAL PARK – Over the last decade, wildfires have ravaged countless acres of the pinyon-juniper woodlands that cover mesa tops in this national park. While the ancient cliff dwellings have sustained only minor damage, the wildfires have created an additional problem.

Vast acres of earth exposed as a result of the wildfires left the region vulnerable to invasion by non-native weedy plants. One of these, the musk thistle, now covers hundreds of acres of land, and its dense numbers are choking off native species.

While park officials are employing a variety of methods to eradicate the musk thistles and other invasive weeds, they want the public to help, too, by not picking the pretty purple flowers. Collecting any plant life is illegal in the park, but park officials are actively urging the more than 500,000 yearly visitors to the park to help them in their efforts to restore the park's natural plant life. Visitors should seriously consider *not* picking just one "souvenir"—a single musk thistle head can contain and spread hundreds of seeds.

From a Ranger's View Discuss how park rangers might view the tourists to Mesa Verde, Yosemite, or other national parks. What types of behavior would the rangers welcome in visitors? What kinds of things would rangers discourage? Together, create a ranger's wish list that describes the ideal park visitor.

Book Links
• *Building Big,* by David Macaulay
• *Chasing Vermeer,* by Blue Balliett **CHALLENGE**

Internet Challenge Help your child search for websites to learn more about other ancient sites, such as Canyon de Chelly and Bandelier National Monuments.

My Journey Home
Family Connection

This week your child is reading *Fossils: A Peek Into the Past,* an informational selection about young people who found fossils practically in their own backyards.

Vocabulary on the Go   The young fossil finder Jared Post was amazed to think that mammoths once walked around his neighborhood. Take a walk with your child and discuss what your area might have looked like when mammoths walked the Earth over 10,000 years ago. Try to use some of these words as you talk about your neighborhood.

previously   legendary   surveyed   advantages   aspects

Dinosaur Facts   With your child, look through a website or an illustrated book about dinosaurs. Learn information about several dinosaurs. Then take turns giving opinions about which one is the most unusual and unique. Support your opinions with several of the facts you learned.

Work with your child to make dinosaur trading cards. Illustrate the front of each card with a picture of a dinosaur. Then write the facts you learned about it on the back.

Toothy Topics   Fossilized teeth help scientists determine what an extinct creature ate. Discuss the different kinds of teeth in your mouths. How do different teeth help you eat different kinds of foods?

Making Fossils Read these directions together, and then make some "fossils." How closely do the fossils resemble the actual items?

Homemade Fossils

What You'll Need

- clean, outdoor soil
- water
- spoon and bowl
- baking sheet
- items to "fossilize" (small shells, acorns, bones)

1. In the bowl, mix the soil with water, a little at a time, until you have a clay-like mud.
2. Make a large mud ball. Push an item into it.
3. Flatten the ball into a disk about 1-inch thick, keeping the item completely covered with mud.
4. Place the disk on the baking sheet. Repeat with other items.
5. Let the disks dry in a sunny place. When completely dry, break them open with your hands. Gently remove the "fossils."

What's in a Name? Scientists named the fossil remains of ancient creatures using Greek and Latin word parts. Together, use a dictionary or an online resource to find the original sources of words such as *fossil, dinosaur, reptile,* or *Tyrannosaurus rex.* How do the original word parts relate to the descriptions of the creatures or objects?

Book Links
- *The Dinosaurs of Waterhouse Hawkins,* by Barbara Kerley
- *With a Little Luck,* by Dennis B. Fradin **CHALLENGE**

Internet Challenge When did the Ice Age take place? What makes the Jurassic Era different from the Cretaceous? Together, search the Internet to find out how scientists classify different time periods.

My Journey Home
Family Connection

This week your child is reading *Fossil Fish Found!* an informational selection about the surprising sighting of a fish believed to have been extinct for millions of years.

Vocabulary on the Go   The selection describes the discovery of a very odd sea creature. What's the strangest animal you have ever seen? With your child, take turns telling about your sightings. Use as many of these words as you can to tell about the animals.

incredibly   record   insights   destination   suspense

House Detectives   Your child has also read a story this week in which the characters solve a mystery. Hide an object in your house. Then give your child clues about its whereabouts. Challenge your child to use the clues to draw a conclusion about where the object is. Then trade places.

It's Extinct   Help your child use books or the Internet to find out about another extinct animal, such as the saber-toothed cat, the giant sloth, or the moa. When did the animal live? What caused it to become extinct? How do we know that the animal existed at one time?

Work with your child to make a "Lost" poster for the extinct animal. Include information to help people recognize the animal if they see it.

A Cloud of Birds Together, read and discuss this eyewitness account from 1895 of a huge flock of now extinct passenger pigeons.

The Passenger Pigeon

In the 1800s, the passenger pigeon was probably the most common bird on Earth. Some estimates suggest that billions of these birds lived in North America. Hunted to extinction by man, the last passenger pigeon died in captivity in 1914. Only twenty years earlier, this 1895 account describes a huge flock, which sometimes stretched across the sky for over a mile.

"I was startled by hearing a gurgling, rumbling sound, as though an army of horses laden with sleigh bells was advancing through the deep forest toward me. As I listened more intently, I concluded that instead of the trampling of horses, it was distant thunder; yet the morning was clear, calm, and beautiful. Nearer and nearer came the strange comingling of sounds of sleigh bells, mixed with the rumbling of an approaching storm. While I gazed in astonishment, I beheld moving toward me, in an unbroken front, millions of pigeons, the first I had seen that season. They passed like a cloud through the branches of the high trees, through the underbrush and over the ground, apparently overturning every leaf . . . They fluttered all about me, lighting on my head and shoulders; gently I caught two in my hands. . . ."

Limits or Not? Imagine you are both living in the 1800s. Take sides and debate whether limits are needed on hunting passenger pigeons.

Book Links
- *Emi and the Rhino Scientist,* by Mary Kay Carson
- *All of the Above: A Novel,* by Shelley Pearsall **CHALLENGE**

Internet Challenge Help your child use the Internet to find groups that are working to prevent the extinction of certain animals. What measures are they taking to save the species? How can others help?

My Journey Home
Family Connection

Your child is reading a myth, *Journey to Cuzco*, that tells of the quest for the perfect site on which to found the Incan civilization.

Vocabulary on the Go In this week's selection, two Incan siblings set out on an important journey. With your child, discuss a journey that your family has gone on or would like to go on. Try to use some of these words as you tell about your trip.

disadvantage   nerve   pace   barrier   undoubtedly

Amazing Mazes One of the selections your child read this week tells about different kinds of mazes, which are like puzzles. Discuss the following idea with your child: *Many people like puzzles.* Ask your child to share details that explain why this is true.

Getting From Here to There Arriving at a destination takes good directions and navigation skills. Test yours! Take turns dictating a set of directions to a specific spot in your home. Use each other's directions to find out where you end up. What went wrong—or right?

Work together to write a set of directions to a place near your home. Challenge family or friends to use the directions to get to the spot.

Legends of the Sun Read and discuss this Roman myth with your child. In it, a journey ends badly for a careless young boy.

Phaeton and the Chariot

The youth Phaeton was the half-mortal son of the Sun-god. He traveled to the Palace of the Sun to finally meet his father. Phaeton approached the Sun-god and spoke with courage. "My mother tells me you are my father. Is this so?" The Sun-god smiled kindly. "Yes, my son, it is so. How might I prove it?"

Boldly, Phaeton demanded to drive the Sun-god's chariot to light the new day. His father urged Phaeton to choose differently; driving his chariot, the Sun-god knew, would require more strength than the youth possessed. But Phaeton insisted. The Sun-god relented.

As the chariot flew skyward, Phaeton realized that he could not control its powerful, fiery horses. The chariot swung wildly off its course, scorching the world below. The gods called upon their ruler, Jove, to bring an end to the destruction. With a heavy heart, Jove heaved a lightning bolt at the chariot. Phaeton fell to his death, like a shooting star.

By the side of a river, Phaeton was laid to rest. His sisters came to mourn him. There, they were transformed into poplar trees, to bend and grieve forever for their young, foolish brother.

More Myths Use library books or the Internet to find more Roman creation myths. What happens in the myths? What do they explain?

Book Links
- *Amaterasu: Return of the Sun,* by Paul D. Storrie
- *National Geographic Investigates: Ancient Africa,* by Victoria Sherrow **CHALLENGE**

Internet Challenge The ruins of Machu Picchu in Peru give a fascinating glimpse into the lives of the ancient Incans. Together, search the Internet for images and information about this site and its history.